". . . And *WHERE* will you build this 'ALCAN HIGHWAY'?!!"

A COLLECTION OF LETTERS FROM A HOMESICK GI

". . . And *WHERE* will you build this 'ALCAN HIGHWAY'?!!"

For information, write to: Black Horse Publishing
Box 6150, Whitehorse, YT. Y1A 5L7   Canada

ISBN   0-9696114-0-4
CIP   HE356.A4A53 1992   388.1'09798   C92-091343-1

". . . And *WHERE* will you build this 'ALCAN HIGHWAY'?!!"

Illustrations By
CATHERINE DEER
Text By
DANIEL ST-JEAN

BLACK HORSE PUBLISHING
Whitehorse, Canada

We dedicate this book to the
thousands of men and women,
civilians and troops who worked
on the construction of the

ALASKA HIGHWAY
and in particular

Robert E. Hayes
Robert Ormbrek   **Jim Muncy**
Ribot Valiton   **Robert L. Seaton**

(all with the 18th Combat Engineers Regiment)

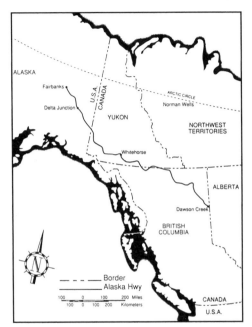

ALASKA

Fairbanks

Delta Junction

U.S.A. / CANADA

ARCTIC CIRCLE

Norman Wells

YUKON

NORTHWEST TERRITORIES

Whitehorse

ALBERTA

Dawson Creek

BRITISH COLUMBIA

——— Border
——— Alaska Hwy

100 0 100 200 Miles
100 0 100 200 Kilometers

CANADA

U.S.A.

About the Alaska Highway

Until World War II, there was no direct land route from the lower United States to the Yukon or Alaska, although plans for building a road to the North had been envisioned by both the Canadian and the American governments.

The Japanese bombings of Pearl Harbor and later Dutch Harbor changed all that. The Alaska Territory and its population of 72,000 suddenly gained important status as a strategic military outpost. To quote a well-known Canadian journalist of the time, George Murry,

"We will either build a highway up to Alaska or the Japanese will build it down for us." After much deliberation, the present route to the North was selected. The Prairie Route, as it was called then, was chosen because the strategic location of airfields along the North West Staging Route would enable the U.S. Army to deliver equipment and supplies necessary to build the road into the Far North.

In the agreement between the two nations, Canada agreed to furnish the right of way and to supply the materials. The Americans agreed to provide the manpower and the equipment, to pay for the construction and to eventually turn over the Canadian portion of the road to the Canadian Government. Native Indians, trappers and prospectors were hired to assist the U.S. army surveyors. Bush pilots ferried men and supplies, and riverboats went into high gear delivering equipment to camps along the route.

Construction began on March 9, 1942, a week after the first U.S. troops had disembarked at Dawson Creek, B.C. The U.S. Army Engineers were deployed with the job of building the pioneer road through mostly wilderness. These men had the task of conquering not only the machines to build the road but the three M's — mosquitoes, muskeg and mud.

Hardship and heroism built the Highway. At the peak of construction, 11,500 troops, 7,500 civilians and 11,000 pieces of equipment worked on the road. Working three eight-hour shifts, seven days a week, the men battled not only the elements but fatigue, a lack of supplies and extremely poor living conditions. Many lives were lost as a result of hypothermia and from accidents related to the construction work.

For Whitehorse, which had been designated the northern headquarters of the Alaska Canada Military Highway it began on Friday, April 3, 1942, when a longer version of the scheduled White Pass

train steamed into the Front Street (now 1st Avenue) depot. The local citizens watched in amazement as 150 members of 'A' Company, 18th Combat Engineers, U.S. Army, poured off the train.

Within one month, its population of 650 swelled to more than 3,000. The men, their construction equipment and supplies just kept arriving. A city had been created where a village once stood.

Due to the unexpected increase in demand, Whitehorse stores were sold out most of the time. That included the liquor store. Two boxcars of beer lasted a single day. After that you did without until the next shipment arrived from Vancouver. Bootlegging flourished. A $5 bottle of rye whiskey would fetch $30 or more at work camps along the highway.

The two groups working south from Whitehorse and north from Dawson Creek met at Contact Creek, B.C. on September 24, 1942, six and a half months after construction began.

The other two groups, working north from Whitehorse and south from Alaska met at Beaver Creek, Y.T. on October 20.

To officially open the highway, a ceremony was held at Soldier's Summit near Kluane Lake in the Yukon on November 20, 1942. A time of eight and a half months from the beginning of construction.

When originally completed, the end to end distance was 1,522 miles (2,450 kms). "Construction of the Alaska Highway was the greatest and fastest engineering feat of our century," (Walter Raedeke).

For the people, the land and the communities along the route, the impacts were permanent — some good and some bad. A new link was opened for transportation and communication with the "Outside". For the native, it brought changes to a traditional lifestyle that was dependent on the land. The memory of that amazing time lives forever with those who experienced it.

NAME: Gᴇᴏʀɢᴇ Iꜱᴀᴀᴄ **JOE**

AGE: 20   **HEIGHT:** 6′2″ (188 cm)
WEIGHT: 220 LBS. (100 kg)
HAIR: Dark Brown   **EYES:** Brown
HOMETOWN: Greenville

FAMILY: Father - Oral Wallace Joe
Mother - Pearl Joe
Oldest of 4 brothers (Cliff, Harold & Cyril) and
4 sisters (Lillian, Rose, Betsy, Sadie)

LOVE INTEREST: None at the moment (although he finds the redhead who works at the Greenville post office very attractive).

TRAITS: Cheerful, positive attitude, hard worker, reliable, organized, honest, non-smoker and (before this assignment) non-drinker.

LIKES: Greenville, sports, dogs, redheads, mom's baking (and in particular her raisin oatmeal cookies), spiders (would like a pet tarantula), music and movies ("Gone With The Wind" is his favorite).

DISLIKES: (Before this assignment) Being away from Greenville. (After this assignment) Corned Willie, curling, powdered eggs, Vienna Sausage, hot cakes, mosquitoes, rain, mud, snow, eating outdoors, showering outdoors, tents, playing poker, washing dishes, commanding officers (most), cross-cut saws, heat waves, cold spells, bugles, windy narrow dirt roads, and especially G.I. GOLDFISH CAKES!

Dear Mother,

This past week has been frantic but today being Sunday, I finally have some time to myself to tell you what has happened since Monday when I sent the letter from Alaska.

I'm now in Whitehorse (it's in the Yukon, Canada). My company left Skagway Friday morning. All of us got on board that old White Pass train that was used by gold seekers some forty years ago.

First the train travelled through the woods where I saw lots of waterfalls. Then it started to climb, and it climbed and climbed until we reached the Summit at White Pass. It was white alright, snow everywhere!

I think the engineer was going slow on purpose to give us soldiers a chance to admire the scenery.

I really enjoyed the ride. It was nice to relax for awhile after the frenzy of the past few days.

Just before we arrived here Sarge Ormbrek was telling me that the village should be pretty quiet this time of the year because the Yukon River is still frozen in places and the riverboats are not running yet. And since there is no road out of here, the people hibernate for six months of the year.

So he figured that the arrival of a trainfull of soldiers coming to build a highway could really get the locals excited.

Well by gosh, he was right! We pulled into the station in the middle of the afternoon and even though it was a fair bit breezy the town folk turned out in droves to give us a warm and enthusiastic welcome.

Now it wasn't quite the Fourth of July in Greenville, Mom, but it sure felt good to be greeted in that fashion!

Well, after all that excitement we gathered our gear, formed a column and walked up Main Street under cheers and applause from the crowd. We finally made it to the other end of town where we climbed to the top of an escarpment located near the airfield. It's a beautiful view of the valley from here.

I was assigned a spot on the bivouac site where I got to meet my three "roommates"; their names are Bob, John and Dick. We welcomed each other and got busy staking out our tent. As is customary in the Army, it all went pretty smoothly.

The tents weren't exactly what the C.O. had ordered but as the Sarge pointed out, "Small detail!" He assured us that the regulation bell tents would show up eventually and suggested that in the meantime we adapt.

CATHERINE DEE '92

And adapt we did. After all, we're the Engineer Corps, we're trained to think on our feet.

In any event, we were so tired the first night we all slept like babies. Besides, the close quarters made the tent quite warm and when some of the guys started to snore in harmony, it reminded me of that wonderful train ride.

You know what Dad always says, "Happiness is going to sleep in a soft, clean, cosy bed after an honest day's work."

I was one of the first to wake up the next morning and when I looked around, the scene brought back memories of Christmases past when Uncle Fred and Uncle Abner would visit and all of us kids would go to sleep in the same room . . .

Anyway, all is well here and I'm looking forward to starting work tomorrow.

My love to all,

George

P.S. Happy birthday Harold! And happy belated birthday to you Lilly. (Sorry . . .)

Sunday, April 12th, 1942

Dear Mother,

The camp is completely set up now and it's quite comfortable. I'm enjoying it up here, especially mealtimes.

We eat outside most of the time and it reminds me of those picnics us kids used to have with you and dad and Uncle Abner, except that army chow is not quite like your home cooking, Mom, but it's good.

Also, the weather is not exactly like June back home but I hear it will get warmer soon.

Breakfast is especially pleasant. Everyone is in a good mood after having had a good night's sleep. (Except maybe the kitchen staff who have to start work at 4:00 am.)

But yesterday our cook was all smiles. He thinks he may have discovered a new kind of weapon. The only problem is it only works in cold temperatures so he needs to work on it a bit more before he goes to the C.O. I'll keep you posted.

Love

George

P.S. My bath towel has a hole in it and the soap is kinda rough. Please . . .

Dear Mother,

All is well in the "Land of the Midnight Sun" (that's what the locals call this part of the country).

Speaking of locals, we finally got the chance to meet some of them officially this past week. The Sarge brought a whole bunch of maps and plans along and I could tell he really impressed them all. Except for one skeptical old-timer who kept asking, "Where will you build this 'Alcan Highway'?" Anyway, they showed great enthusiasm for our project and offered to help us. I think one trapper fellow summed up the feelings of the group when he said, "The sooner the road is done, the sooner you boys can go home again."

It seems they have genuine concern for our well-being. They suggested that the best way to break the ice between us and them would be to have a friendly game of curling.

So we played last night. Was it ever fun, Mom! Curling is a lot like horseshoes except it's played on ice. Two teams of four people get out there with their brooms and throw rocks from one end of the rink to the other. The rock that gets closest to the bull's eye scores the point.

It's a very relaxing game that requires precision and concentration. It allows the players lots of time for conversation and, as it is not a contact sport, it's a great way to make new friends.

Minor disagreements occur sometimes when measurements are required to decide who scored the points but they are always resolved in a neighborly fashion.

The locals won of course. As a gesture of friendship, we offered to meet them again this summer for baseball.

I played an intense game last night and my arm's a bit sore so I'll tell you more next week.

Affection to all

George

Sunday, April 26th, 1942

Hello Mother,

Got your first parcel last Monday. Thank you for the wool socks and the cookies. I have to hide them as Dick has a sweet tooth too. Thanks for the newsy letter too. And Mom, put away your worry-beads. Everything is A-ok up here! I'm having a swell time!

I went downtown on Tuesday and as I neared the train depot I heard some beautiful music. When I got there I saw our band performing to an enthusiastic crowd of music lovers. I think I recognized some of the folks from a couple of weeks ago. Sure is nice to see local support for our activities.

The crowd had a swinging good time and I think the band did too. Even the dogs seemed to enjoy the sounds of the trumpet.

I'll leave you on that note. Give my love to all and wish Grandpa Archie a swift recovery for me.

George

Sunday, May 10th, 1942

Hello Mother,

Sorry I skipped a week but we had to lay down a lot of corduroy last Sunday so I had no time to write.

The first Army payroll rolled into town last Wednesday and I got to help Dick and Bob carry the bags of money from the train to the bank. The bank manager was a bit surprised at the size of the deposit but he 'managed' quite well just the same.

He was quick to point out that there hadn't been a holdup in the Yukon since the early 1900's. "You couldn't get out of the territory with your loot and you couldn't spend it all up here," he said, "so, why bother?"

I agree with him about the 'no place to spend it' part so I'm sending $19.00 from my $21.00 monthly pay for you to put aside for when I return.

But why think about my return now? I just got here! Life in the army is great and the chow is swell. The locals are friendly, the scenery is spectacular and the weather isn't bad at all.

The days are long and it gets quite warm in the afternoon. The grass is green and there are flowers everywhere.

But the weather up here can change quickly sometimes (just like the mood of the C.O.). Last Thursday we went to bed under a clear sky and woke up the next morning with some new snow. It was just a few flakes, mind you, so it didn't stay more than a couple of hours.

Everything's back to normal now. I'll talk to you again next week.

Love   *George*

P.S. Make Cliff promise not to marry his Angela until I return sometime next spring.

CATHERINE DEER '92 ©

27

Hello Mother,

I'm writing to you from the mess tent this morning because there is a crew doing some work around our tent site at the moment.

Until yesterday the weather had been pretty nice. You might recall we had a bit of snow ten days ago but it was nothing to write home about.

Well it started to rain lightly last evening. From what I hear though it turned into a downpour during the night. I never even noticed because the gentle sound of the rain on the canvas had put me right to sleep.

And, as the Sarge said this morning while he was hanging his laundry up to dry: "The army's got the best darned tents money can buy and thanks to the engineer's knowledge of soil p-e-r-m-e-a-b-i-l-i-t-y, we have nothing to fear from a few drops of rain."

Other than the weather, everything's under control.

Hugs and kisses

George

P.S. Send more cookies, please!

Hello Mom,

Remember how I told you last week about that bit of rain we had? Well it started again on Sunday night and it rained nonstop for almost three days.

But then, as the Sarge always says, "We'll build this road come hell or high water!"

Thank goodness nothing like that happened . . . That little downpour didn't stop us from working though. We spent most of Monday installing culverts and ditches to drain off the excess rainwater. Then on Tuesday we completed that bridge we've been working on for the past ten days.

The guys are so ingenious; there isn't a brook, a creek or a river they can't span.

This highway was only supposed to be a 'pioneer road to Alaska', but the way we're constructing it, using nothing but the best materials and the latest technology, it'll be around for a long time to come.

It finally stopped raining Wednesday afternoon.

On Thursday the Sarge gave me a bunch of surveyor's equipment to deliver about five miles up the road. Boy, all that rain sure makes driving a Jeep a real skill test! (But you've seen me with machinery, Mom. The word 'impassable' is not in my vocabulary!)

It took most of the day to accomplish my mission but I got the job done just the same. I had no reason to worry because I knew I could always count on my resourceful buddies in the unlikely event that I should encounter any minor problems.

I got back to camp around 7 pm, parked the Jeep, ate supper and polished my boots. Then I took a long, hot, relaxing shower and headed off to bed with a good book. Life doesn't get much better than this!

Love, and more love

George

P.S. No, Uncle Harold, you can't just bend down and pluck gold nuggets off the streets here. The Gold Rush happened over 40 years ago and it took place in Dawson City some 300 miles north of here.

33

Hello Mom,

Had to work again last Sunday. The whole tent missed reveille so we had to skip breakfast. Then we laid down corduroy all day and didn't get back until 7:30 pm. I was so hungry I ate two servings even though Cream of Corned Willie was on the menu.

Dick didn't care for it at all so he decided to cook his own dinner. He borrowed a pot, two cans of beans and luncheon meat, and came back to the tent. He was in such a hurry he decided to use Petrol to light the stove.

Somehow his actions got the attention of the C.O. who came over to investigate. He seemed to be impressed with Dick's attempt at home cooking and suggested that maybe he should practice on a larger scale and put his talent to good use for the benefit of the rest of the camp.

35

However, Dick pointed out that he was afflicted with a skin condition that prevents him from handling other people's food. The C.O. then insisted that one of us take Dick's place for a week of kitchen duty. I volunteered.

For the last six days now I've been assisting the chef to prepare three meals a day for the whole company. We are a bit limited in what we can cook but we manage to put together an interesting and varied menu for the guys. See for yourself:

MONDAY: Pancakes / Beef Slum / Corned Beef Hash
TUESDAY: Hot Cakes / Corned Willie / Baked Beans
WEDNESDAY: Fried Eggs / Vienna Sausage / Goldfish Cakes
THURSDAY: Hot Cakes / Cream of Corned Willie / Hamburgers

. . . and so on for the rest of the week.

Who knows, Mom? Dick's absent-mindedness may have opened up a whole new career for me when I'm done with the army. Only time will tell . . .

George

P.S. Tell Aunt Ursula that there are no igloos, Eskimos or polar bears in the Yukon. At least not where we are . . .

Hello Mom,

Please put this $13.00 aside for me.

Now with the exciting news for today . . . I'm finished with my apprenticeship for now (just as I was getting good at it too . . .)

On Wednesday the C.O. assigned me to the Regimental Port Exchange (PX for short). I'll be looking after the warehouse and selling goods to army personnel. Selling is fun but keeping goods on the shelves isn't easy.

You see, before we arrived here the population was just under 700. Now Whitehorse has become a garrison town of over 3,000 and due to the unexpected increase in demand, the stores as well as the PX are sold out most of the time.

When they have goods to sell there are long lineups. I encountered one of those last Monday and had to wait almost an hour to buy some medicine to take care of my cold.

CATHERINE DEER —92 ©

But as luck would have it, just as I was being told that stock had run out, I got word that a boxcar full of supplies was rolling into town.

Knowing the urgency of getting the supplies to the various stores, a dozen guys generously volunteered their assistance.

We all walked over to the depot and sat waiting patiently while someone checked the waybills. When all was in order, I helped to unload the goods and carry them over to the TAYLOR and DRURY store.

It was hard work but I didn't mind. I was rewarded with a cold bottle of Coca-Cola and a smile from the owner's daughter.

By the way, Mom, next time you're in the post office be sure and tell the redhead at the counter Private George sends his regards.

Until next Sunday, love and kisses,

George

P.S. The medicine worked well and I'm no longer under the weather.

Hello Mom,

Well, I guess I won't have to worry about lineups for awhile. Last Monday the whole company hit the road and moved northwest about 150 miles to a new camp on the shores of Kluane Lake.

They say the fishing here is good. I hope I get a chance to cast a line or two this summer.

I've also heard that wildlife is abundant in these parts but we've been here a week and so far I haven't seen any. Unless of course you include mosquitoes in the wildlife population. There are a few of those around but they don't bother us much. Maybe our blood is too thick.

I hear the guys working in Alaska have to wear campaign hats equipped with mosquito nets so they don't swallow the puny pests. We won't need those here. In any event, the little critters should only be around for another week or two.

Last night just as l was getting ready for bed, two rather large specimens landed on my leg. l flattened them immediately and brushed them off onto the bed covers.

Dick looked at them and said, "I'd sure hate to meet the mother of those twins!" l guess that thought must have stayed with me in my sleep.

l dreamed that after the twins' 'funeral' the parents started to chase me around the cemetery. The 'dad' caught up and injected me with a serum that shrunk me to the size of a flea.

Then came 'mom'. l ran into the bush as fast as l could but l couldn't escape. Just as she was about to sting me and probably suck every drop of blood out of my body, Dick saved me by waking me up.

So from now on it's no more eating sardines or messing around with mosquitoes before bedtime!

l love you all,

George

P.S. Congratulations Rose on your graduation!

45

Hi Mom,

Remember I said something about a career in the restaurant business. . . ? Well, if that doesn't pan out, maybe I'll think about journalism.

Dick has read all my letters to you. He thinks I have 'good writing skills' as well as the 'ability to report the events faithfully'. He says that those are the two best attributes of a great reporter.

So now I'm helping my roommates with their correspondence. It's good practice and it doesn't take too much of my time. I just hope the word doesn't spread.

The only thing that bugs me from time to time is that they want me to sugar-coat their letters so their relatives don't get too worried.

I think that's a lame excuse for telling tales so I told them all this morning: "Just the facts, guys. Just the facts!" I hope they got the message.

Maybe I shouldn't be too hard on them. After all, for months now they've had to go without beer, cards, cigarettes and girls . . . All things considered they're doing pretty good!

Your son *George* reporting!

Hi Mom,

Sorry about last Sunday but we had to work on account we took the 4th of July off.

As part of celebrating Dominion Day on July 1st the locals from nearby Burwash Landing invited us to play a friendly game of "softball". (I got hit twice in the first inning and I can tell you that ball is anything but 'soft'.)

The score was 12-2 in the 7th inning and suddenly they all started to celebrate. When we asked them why we weren't playing nine innings they said that a softball game ends after seven.

The guys were well prepared to argue on that point but I suggested that since it was their park, their game and their holiday, we should just let them win.

The main thing is we had fun with our neighbours. And who knows, maybe we'll play hockey next winter if we're still in these parts.

49

CATHERINE DEER 92 ©

All the same it was way too warm that day to even think about hockey on ice. The only kind of ice we were wishing for was the kind we needed to chill the beer we had in stock for the 4th of July holiday.

The C.O. had ordered a truckfull of beer for the company but the prospect of drinking hot brew was dampening the spirit.

When Sarge heard about our complaints, he suggested that if warm ale wasn't good enough to quench our thirst we could always drink some ice cold lake water.

That's when Bob, one of our brightest engineers, connected the two and devised an ingenious plan to cool our precious cargo in a natural way.

I promised Bob not to reveal his invention in case he decides to patent it but let's just say he saved the day and we all got to enjoy a couple of cold ones.

And as Dad always says, "Happiness is sitting on the veranda sipping a cold beer after an honest day's work." Three cheers to Dad!

The Brigadier General came for a visit in the afternoon and stayed for dinner. In his honor the chef prepared roast beef with mashed potatoes and gravy. Great dinner! I wish he'd visit more often . . .

He had to leave early, which was too bad since some of our guys had put together a great show for him and spent all week rehearsing it.

The rest of us really enjoyed the entertainment anyway. Our band played a few numbers and later accompanied a singer who got the guys all excited with some old favorites. (He had to do "Deep in the Heart of Texas" twice!)

All in all, the good music, great songs, dazzling costumes and lively dancers made for a high caliber performance.

After the production was over, some of us walked down to the mess tent where the Sarge was taking part in a game of gin rummy with his guests.

That gave my buddies the idea to start up their own game. They asked me to be the fourth player and l accepted after they agreed to teach me some of the tricks of the game.

And teach me they did. l seemed to get better and better as the evening wore on. Now l understand what Dad means when he says, "Happiness is playing a friendly game of cards with the neighbors at the end of an honest day's work." l sure did enjoy myself. l'm just sorry l had to work the next morning and had to retire early.

l had a great Fourth of July, Mom. l hope yours was exciting too.

Hugs and Kisses

P.S. l won't be sending any money home this month.

George

Hi Mom,

It's been a fun week, I've seen a lot of wildlife the past few days.

I saw coyotes, eagles, beavers and a wolverine but the best encounter was on Friday. I was sitting on my bulldozer eating lunch when I spotted a big Grizzly bear in the distance. He was light brown with a big hump between his shoulders and looked quite tame.

He just lumbered along beside the creek, stopped for a minute to sniff the air, (probably decided he didn't care for the smell of tunafish) and disappeared into the woods again, very quietly.

It's great to be able to observe such a beautiful animal, especially from a safe distance.

The Sarge says there's nothing to worry about when it comes to wildlife as most animals are real shy and they try hard to avoid humans.

57

Except for porcupines I'm told.

A porcupine looks a bit like a beaver with a bunch of knitting needles sticking out of its back. Dick told me I better run if I see one because if I wander into his territory he might throw his needles at me and they sting like the dickens.

So when one crossed the road I was working on yesterday, I stayed put, didn't move or blink my eyes until he had disappeared from view.

But he must have made an impression on me because last night I dreamed I was being chased by a bunch of these creatures and they were shooting their needles at me. I got hit by one and felt a sharp pain in my side.

Just then I woke up in a sweat and realized I had fallen asleep eating sardines out of a can and had just rolled over onto the fork. What a night!

Love to all,

George

P.S. Have Sadie send it to me. Tell her I know a tooth fairy who will pay two bits for it.

Sunday, July 26th, 1942

Hi Mom,

The temperature got mighty warm this past week. The mercury climbed into the nineties for four days in a row. It's a bit uncomfortable to work in but at least we know it will cool off in the evening when the sun starts to go down.

The warm weather and the lack of mosquitoes have given us a chance to spend practically all our evenings outside where we can take part in group sports and enjoy the fresh air and long hours of daylight. Like Dad often says in the summer, "Happiness is napping in a hammock under a couple of willow trees after an honest day's work in the hot sun."

Fortunately for us, the army tents were designed to protect us from the odd summer heat wave as well as from the rigors of winter.

The cold days of April now seem a distant memory . . .

But we have to keep an eye on our tents because the heat also brings the gophers out of their burrows.

Gophers are what the folks up here call ground squirrels. They have external cheek pouches which they use to carry their food back to their dwellings.

Although they are not considered a nuisance in general, they have two characteristics that make them unwelcome around the camp. They are very impudent and they will steal anything and everything they can lay their little paws on.

Upon returning to my tent last night, I caught one stealing my last oatmeal cookie. I chased him around for half an hour but he got away. I was rather annoyed with these little rodents so I consoled myself by eating a can of Spam before going to bed. You can probably guess what happened after that . . .

But they're so cute you just can't stay mad at them.

Love and Kisses, *George*

P.S. It's called "The Land of the Midnight Sun" because in the summer the sun doesn't set till after midnight.

FISH CAKES

BEANS

Hi Mom,

Last Wednesday l visited with the cook for awhile after dinner. He had a good laugh when l told him about my 'gopher dream'. He laughed even harder when l told him about the one where the porcupines were hunting me down.

It seems Dick was misinformed. Porcupines are very shy and they DO NOT shoot their needles (quills). In fact the natives hunt them for food occasionally and then the women use the quills to decorate garments.

After that informative chat, l finished off the evening with my daily delight; l grabbed one of those scented bars of soap and that big towel you sent and headed off to my favorite shower stall.

The temperature and flow of the water are not always dependable but as Dad always says, "Happiness is coming home to an invigorating shower and a clean towel at the end of a long day's work."

Some of the guys like Dick and Bob don't seem to care much for showers. They'd rather take a bath. So last Friday, just for a change, I went down to the lake with them.

It turned out to be quite a stimulating experience. Kluane Lake is magnificent. From a distance its clean cool water appears turquoise.

As I was splashing about, I thought about what Dad always says in the summer, "Happiness is a refreshing swim in the cool water of the pond after a hard day's work out in the hot sun." He sure would like it here!

My buddies are such comedians, they tried to get me into a contest to see who could walk on water the farthest! I think they were all just homesick for their rubber duckies.

But we all had a great time and you'll be happy to know that I've found one more way to keep my belly button clean.

Love, George

P.S. No Uncle Fred . . . there aren't any golf courses up here (I wouldn't have time to play anyway!).

Sunday, August 9th, 1942

Hi Mom,

I have to tell you about something very strange that happened to me yesterday.

The C.O. gave me the afternoon off and since it was warm and sunny I decided to go fishing. I borrowed Bob's gear, got some instructions, and walked over to the lake.

I sat on the shore and started casting. Within minutes I caught my first fish. Then another one. And another one. There wasn't much room where I was sitting so I just threw them over the bush behind me.

Catching twenty fish in an hour tired me out so I dozed off for awhile. Then I woke up, gathered up my gear, and walked behind the bush to bag my catch — THEY WERE ALL GONE!

The guys swear they didn't play a trick on me and I know I didn't dream this because my hands still smell like fish.

I'll let you know what happened once I've resolved this mystery.

Hugs, hugs, hugs

George

P.S. I'm sending $6.00 for you to keep and the two bits are for Sadie's tooth.

Sunday, August 23rd, 1942

Hello Mom,

You know how Dad always says, ''Happiness is coming home to a delicious meal after an honest day's work.'' Well Dad would feel right at home in this camp.

Every week the guys are given the opportunity to do six honest day's work. And on top of that, no matter how tired they are when quitting time rolls around, they know that a mouth-watering dinner is waiting for them back at camp.

Some people say that variety is the spice of life. Well, if that's the case life in the army can only be described as spicy.

I am constantly amazed by the seemingly endless imagination displayed by the cook and his crew in preparing the daily menu.

The food is always of the highest quality too. The only things missing are fresh fruit and ice cream every now and then.

Although none of us wished to complain about the chow, my buddies and I agreed that adding some wild meat to our menu might spice up our lives a little.

So after work last Wednesday, the four of us went out hunting for game. We figured we had the perfect team since Bob knows these woods like the back of his hand, Dick is a very skilled marksman, John is an apprentice butcher, and as you know, I have some cooking experience.

Well, after just two hours of walking and stalking we had ourselves the makings of a nice dinner.

It's too bad there are no large animals like moose, sheep or mountain goats in the area where the camp is set up; we were so sharp we could have brought back enough wild game for everybody. But we were proud of our achievement all the same.

We don't get to eat much chicken at the camp so this was going to be quite a feast. Dick likes to joke that the reason why the cook calls a certain dish 'Chicken Surprise' is because everyone is really surprised whenever they find a piece of chicken on their plate.

So we sat around the fire while I cooked our dozen plump grouse. Bob told us of his fishing adventures and Dick shared with us his thrill at winning first prize in a shooting competition.

Then John made our mouths water as he recounted his latest visit with his native friends in Burwash Landing when he was served a feast of moose meat, rice, and fried flat bread (called bannock).

I must have learned something during my stint as assistant to the chef because the guys complimented me on the tasty dinner.

We had a wonderful evening. I sure hope we can do it again sometime.

Give my love to all,

George.

P.S. I still can't figure out what happened to my fish two weeks ago!

Hi Mom,

Since I want my long term plans to come true before I'm eighty, I'll have to smarten up and find ways to earn more money.

It seems most other guys manage to pocket extra cash. The ones who don't smoke sell their cigarette allotment and the ones who don't drink sell their beer coupons.

Then, of course, there are professional poker players who hunt for pigeons to pluck after every payday. They won't catch me at that game!

And then there's guys like Tim Mundy, (popularly known as 'The Medicine Man'). Tim claims he used to work for a druggist down in Tennessee before the war. He managed to gather a variety of medicinal ingredients which he uses to make a concoction that's supposed to cure all ailments. He calls it 'Mundy's Mixture' and he makes piles of money selling this stuff to just about every private in the Company. (I'm not planning to buy any . . .)

But I sampled some last night out of curiosity. It didn't taste too bad. I'm not sure, however, about its ability to cure all ailments. Curiosity may not have killed the cat but it sure gave it a bad headache . . .

On a brighter note, I got my first 'up close' look at a moose last week. (Not THAT close, Mom, relax . . .)

A bull moose is a magnificent animal that looks a bit like a horse with a coat-rack on top of its head.

I went to visit John who was doing some survey work. Since I had never looked through such an instrument, he invited me to take a peek. I was fascinated.

For some reason or another, our actions caught the attention of a bull who calmly ambled out of a nearby bush to see what we were up to.

What a beautiful animal! I hear they can move pretty swiftly.

The Sarge says bull moose tend to become a lot more social as 'rutting season'' approaches.

You learn something everyday . . .

Love
George

P.S. Talking about medicine reminded me of Uncle Abner. Has he fully recovered since his liver operation?

Wednesday, September 16th, 1942

Hi Mom,

After Sunday, Saturday is my favorite day of the week.

You see, I always do my laundry on Friday night. That way, on Saturday I can step out of my tent at daybreak and gather up clean clothes that smell like the morning dew. (It reminds me of Dad who always says, "Happiness is putting on clean fresh-smelling clothes before an honest day's work.")

Last Saturday started pretty much like all the others. I shaved, got dressed and passed inspection at 6:00 am. Then came my favorite time of the day; hot cakes for breakfast.

Later on the C.O. called me to the PX office and gave me my travelling papers. I'll be leaving tomorrow to drive down to Watson Lake.

As for my three buddies, they'll be heading north toward Beaver Creek where the 18th is expected to meet with the 97th (working down from Alaska) in the next few weeks thus completing the northern section of the road.

Is that enough exciting news for one letter?

George

P.S. I won't be sending any money home this month, I've invested most of my pay in Mundy's Mixture.

Wednesday, September 23rd, 1942

Bonjour Maman,

I've covered a lot of ground since last Wednesday. I headed out in the jeep on Thursday as planned, and drove south to my first business stop in Destruction Bay.

While I was there I decided to pay a visit to the dentist in residence. What a nice fellow! I was really surprised to find such a highly qualified professional in a post so remote.

He fixed all my fillings in exchange for a bottle of Mundy's Mixture. (That stuff has become quite a popular remedy so I brought along ten bottles to use for bartering.)

From there on, it only took five days to make it to Whitehorse, with several stops along the way. But my Jeep needed repairs so the C.O. had to put me on a transport plane to Watson Lake, where I arrived this afternoon. All is well so far.

Au Revoir

George

P.S. At the dentist, I met a fellow by the name of Ribot Valiton who taught me how to say "Hi, Mom!" and "Goodbye" in French.

83

Hi Mom,

This trip has turned out to be quite an adventure. The day after my last letter, I was conducting business at the PX, when I met Carl, a fellow private from Danville, Illinois, (Company 'D', 341st Engineers). He needed a ride to carry some wood to put up a sign so I gave him a lift.

Later at the restaurant we heard that the team from the south was about to meet the one from the north some 50 miles out of town. Since Carl was on sick leave and I had business nearby we decided to head down there to witness the great event.

What a fantastic spectacle! On the afternoon of October 24th, the southern sector of the road was completed when bulldozer operators of the 35th and 340th Regiments came together at Contact Creek.

Everybody cheered, applauded, and shook hands. It was a memorable occasion.

85

We spent the rest of the day celebrating with the guys.

Our next stop was in Lower Post where I had to do some business with the Hudson's Bay Company. During the two days it took to complete the paperwork, we stayed with a native family who invited us to sample some of their delicacies. (Moose steaks, cariboo roast, bannock, soapberry ice cream and Labrador tea.)

Carl was feeling a little homesick when we got back to Watson Lake so he decided to add his own sign to the signpost he had erected a few days before.

I thought that was a good idea so I got some supplies and put up another post where I hung my own sign. It reads: "I left my heart in Greenville".

As I was driving out of town the next day I noticed that a soldier from Peoria had done the same thing. Who knows? We may have started a trend!

My regards to Greenville

George

P.S. Happy sweet sixteenth Betsy!

Sunday, October 11th, 1942

Hi Mom,

Today I'm writing to you from Teslin. I've driven about 150 miles and made numerous stops since I wrote to you last week from Upper Liard.

The road is actually very good. It's just that we can't drive fast because it's a bit crooked and there are numerous hills and one-lane bridges along the way. But the guys have done a great job!

You asked me about 'corduroy' so here's an explanation. In the North, most of the top soil is 'muskeg' (pretty swampy stuff). About three feet below that, the ground is solid because it's frozen year-round (hence the name 'permafrost').

At first the engineers were removing the muskeg. This exposed the permafrost which thawed out, creating impassable conditions. But they soon learned their lesson.

Now they cut thousands of trees and lay them side by side across the roadbed (it looks something like corduroy). Then they cover the whole thing with gravel and we have a highway . . .

Love you all,

George

P.S. Congratulations Cyril on winning the Spelling Bee — way to go little brother!

Sunday, October 18th, 1942

Hello Mom,

Well I'm finally back at the camp. It's been an exhausting 5 weeks on the road, but exciting all the same. The road was pretty good all the way to Whitehorse where I spent a couple of days.

After that there was one last stop in Champagne, a native community 50 miles west of Whitehorse. There's a PX and a medical facility in the village.

I was sitting in the waiting room chatting with some of the guys when a good-looking nurse walked in. She was nice and sweet and did all she could to catch our attention but we kept our cool and politely acknowledged her presence.

That was the first time in months I was close enough to a woman to be able to smell her perfume.

Those guys in Champagne don't know how lucky they are to have female company! I can't wait to see the redhead again.

I miss you all, love

George

P.S. I read Miss Hepburn gives a great performance in "Woman of the Year". Have you seen it yet?

Hi Mom,

My roommates came back on Friday after being away for seven weeks. They told me they were in Beaver Creek on October 20th when the two teams met to complete the northern sector of the road.

They described a spectacle almost identical to the one I saw in Contact Creek; soldiers cheering, applauding, shaking hands and taking pictures. Another great celebration!

The whole tent missed reveille on Saturday so the Sarge confined us to camp for a week. But Saturday night was Halloween so Dick snuck out and headed down to Burwash.

Although he was a bit intoxicated when he returned at 2 am, he still managed to slip past the MP's and get into bed without waking anyone.

Then he turned over and found himself face-to-face with the skull of a moose that Bob had planted on his pillow. Dick screamed so loud he woke up the Sarge and wound up with a week's worth of KP duty. Quite the night for Dick!

Hugs and kisses,

George

P.S. Pastor Privett? What happened to Father McCaffrey?

93

Sunday, November 15th, 1942

Hello,

You'd better sit down Mom, because I've got some news that will knock your socks off.

The big-wigs of the army and the two governments will be holding a ceremony on November 20th at Soldiers' Summit, not far from here. Also attending the event will be one private from each unit that has been working on the construction of the northern sector of the highway.

Can you guess who's been chosen by the C.O. to represent Company 'A' of the 18th Engineers? If you guessed ME, you're right! I'm so excited I could fly!

To prepare for the occasion the Sarge sent me to the PX in Destruction Bay to get a brand new uniform. While I was there I stopped in to see the resident barber. What a nice fellow!

He gave me a shave and a spiffy haircut in exchange for a bottle of Mundy's Mixture. Now I look like Rhett Butler . . .

Your son the 'STAR'

George

P.S. Betsy, the 'boots' you are talking about are called 'mukluks'. Just tell me what size you wear . . .

95

Sunday, November 22nd, 1942

Hi Mom,

I just returned late last night from the opening ceremonies of the highway at Soldiers' Summit. It was great!

I took lots of pictures and had conversations with some of the brass present at that historic moment, including the acting Governor of Alaska, E.L. Bartlett.

There was a contingent from the Royal Canadian Mounted Police as well as privates from all the Companies.

Father Charles read the invocation just before the ribbon was cut and in typical army fashion, everything went as planned. It was a beautiful and touching ceremony. Even the weather cooperated.

Brigadier General James J. O'Connor addressed the crowd. He said that we should all be extremely proud of our accomplishments. He also said we had all been 'Cheechakos' when we first arrived here last spring but that now we had earned the privilege of being referred to as full-fledged 'Sourdoughs'. I'll never forget that day!

Your Sourdough son, *George*

P.S. 'Cheechako' is what the locals call a newcomer. A 'Sourdough' is someone who has spent at least one winter up here, a 'veteran'.

97

Hi Mom,

I'm so excited I couldn't wait 'till Sunday to write. Besides, I won't be here on Sunday; the whole company is going home for the holidays! I'll be home for Christmas, Mom!!

The other good news is that the road is in good shape. A Greyhound bus arrived yesterday from Edmonton, Alberta. That's 1,200 miles away and it only took 48 hours to get here. Wow!

And to top it off, last night we got reacquainted with the 'curlers' we met last spring. When they found out we were leaving they challenged us to a game of hockey.

I guess they felt bad because we were away all summer and never got the chance to play softball with them.

And guess what? We won!!! Final score: 7-6. It was an intense game but us guys were so charged up about going home we could have taken on the Montreal Canadiens!

Well, it sure was fun and a most fitting end to a wonderful relationship with the locals.

Can't wait to see you all

George

P.S. On your next visit to the Post Office, could you let out to the redhead that I'll be home for the holidays . . .

Tuesday, December 15th, 1942

Hi Mom,

This is my last letter from the North. It will go out on the plane tomorrow. I'm sure you will receive it before I arrive home.

I'll be travelling every day from now on. If all goes well the next "Hi Mom", will be at your front door just before Christmas. So make sure you cook a BIG turkey.

I remember Dad saying, "Happiness is sharing a wonderful Christmas dinner with loving relatives and gracious guests" so I'm bringing one along with me.

He longed to see Greenville and I wanted you to meet a real Sourdough. So, here we come, presents and all (not to mention a few surprises)!

When we drove through Watson Lake yesterday I counted over 30 signs. I think the sign post idea is catching on.

I have to stop at every PX between here and Dawson Creek where I will deliver all the books and records to the headquarters.

I've spent most of today dealing with the PX here in Lower Post. The local natives make beautiful crafts with beads and quills. (I bought some gifts for the women in my family.)

Because of the depth of the snow in the village, I couldn't drive the Jeep to the store but a very nice young native fellow by the name of Alfred Jakesta gave me my first ride in a dogsled. It was thrilling.

We're back on the road tomorrow. I'm glad I decided to bring a friend along; one can get pretty lonesome driving for 10 to 12 hours a day on this lonely road. But at least it's in good shape. The ground is frozen solid so I don't have to deal with all the mud I encountered on my previous trip.

With a little help from my 'guardian angel', getting home should be a piece of cake!

Love

George

P.S. Speaking of sweets, do you think maybe you could make a double batch of your raisin oatmeal cookies for our guest . . .?

CATHERINE DEER_92

EPILOGUE

On December 23rd, George and his 'surprises' finally arrived home to a heartwarming reunion of friends and family, making Christmas dinner that year a most memorable celebration.

After a two week leave of absence, George was sent to the Aleutian Islands where he spent the next ten months constructing a port and a landing strip.

He left the army in 1946 and returned home to Greenville where he married Emily in June of the same year. Together they raised six beautiful red-haired children (naming their first son Richard).

In 1965, they moved to Marion, a 'big town' thirty miles away to open "Cheechako", a family restaurant that has earned a reputation for serving the best sourdough hotcakes in the country. (No fishcakes of any kind on the menu.)

This summer George is anxiously planning a return trip to the North with his family to show them his greatest accomplishment.

So be on the lookout for a big white motorhome with the words: "I LEFT MY HEART IN GREENVILLE" painted on the back . . . Oh yes, and if you look close enough you'll see a handwritten bumpersticker that reads:

"I DROVE THE ALCAN HIGHWAY IN '42
- AND LIVED TO TELL ABOUT IT TOO!"